JOHANN NEPOMUK HUMMEL

SIXTEEN SHORT PIECES

Edited by Timothy Roberts

THE ASSOCIATED BOARD OF
THE ROYAL SCHOOLS OF MUSIC

INTRODUCTION

Johann Nepomuk Hummel (1778-1837) was one of the outstanding Austrian contemporaries of Beethoven. A child prodigy and pupil of Mozart, he became famous throughout Europe as a virtuoso pianist, noted especially for his superb extemporizations. Though his technique was phenomenal – he once had his audience standing on their seats to watch his double trills – he nevertheless preserved a Classical style of playing at a time when pianists like Dussek, Field and Chopin were exploring a more Romantic, 'personal' idiom.

Four of the pieces printed here come from Hummel's *6 pièces très faciles*, Op.52, composed around 1815 and published as part of his series *Repertoire de musique pour les dames* (Nos.5, 7, 9 & 12). (The other two pieces in this opus are a tiny 'cadenza' and an insubstantial ecossaise.) The rest of the volume has been selected from the first part of Hummel's massive piano tutor (*Klavierschule*), printed by Haslinger of Vienna in 1828 and published in an English edition the following year. Many of the pieces in this work are merely brief exercises, but the more extended ones are attractive and poetic miniatures.

The pieces in the *Klavierschule* were fully fingered by the composer, and it proved possible – with a few exceptions – to retain his fingering for the present edition. The works from Op.52 are unfingered in the original, and the fingering printed here is editorial. Other editorial additions to the original text are indicated by small print, square brackets or (in the case of slurs and ties) by a small vertical stroke. The sources use the wedge and dot interchangeably to indicate *staccato*; since the wedge had not yet acquired its modern meaning of an accent, only dots are used in this edition.

It is impossible here to summarize the wealth of interesting information contained in the *Klavierschule*; but it is especially noteworthy that Hummel states that the sustaining pedal should *never* be used, except for special effects in conjunction with the *una corda* pedal in slow movements.

Editorial metronome speeds are printed at the end of each piece; these should be regarded as no more than a suggestion.

TIMOTHY ROBERTS
London 1984

Andante in D

Klavierschule, no.26

[♩.=c.66]

Allegretto in F

Klavierschule, no.46

D.S. al Fine

$[\,\jmath.=c.76]$

Allegretto in D

Klavierschule, no.47

The melody in bars 1, 5 and 9 (l.h.) was originally slurred as follows:

[♩=c.69]

Gigue in D

Klavierschule, no.40

Romance in G

Op.52 no.4

AB 1853

[♩=c.80]

Rondo in F

Klavierschule, no.51

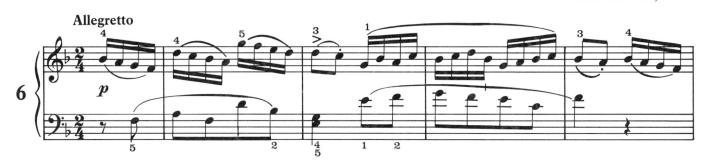

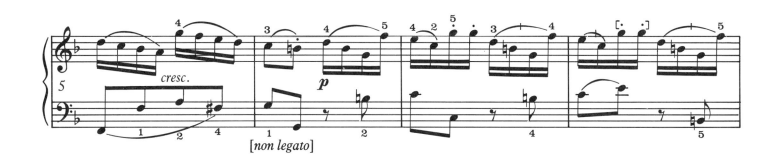

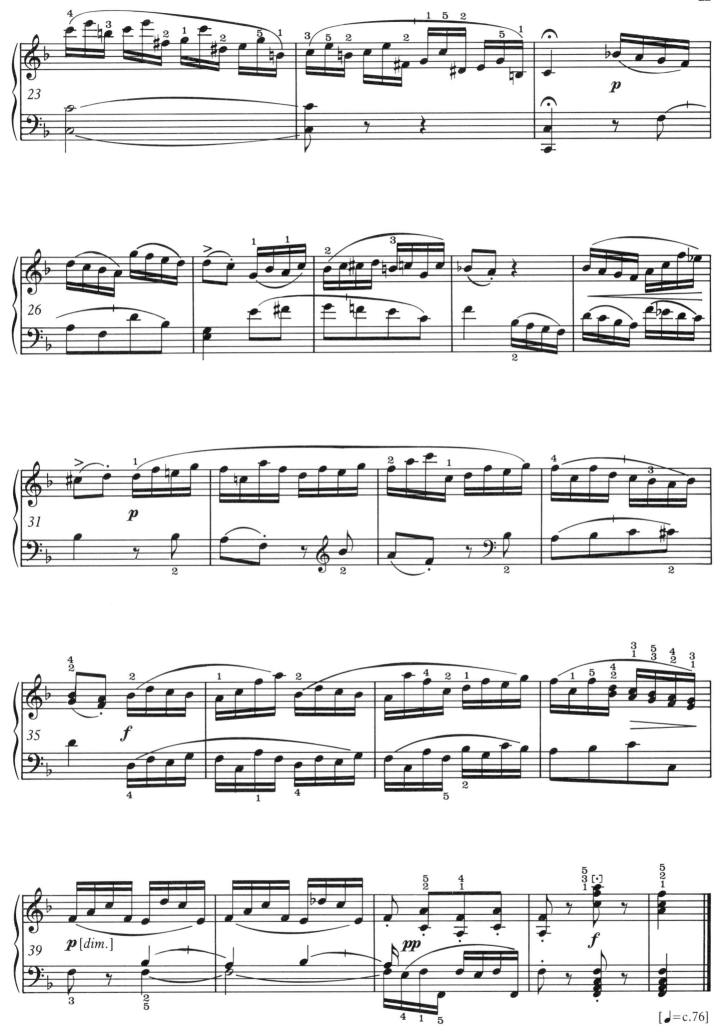

Tempo di Menuetto in C

Op.52 no.3

[♩=c.112]

Andantino in A flat

Klavierschule, no.57

★ ⟍ in the original.

Allegro in C

Op. 52 no. 2

*The slurs may imply use of the sustaining pedal here.

[♩=c.132]

Allegretto in G

Un poco allegretto

Klavierschule, no.48

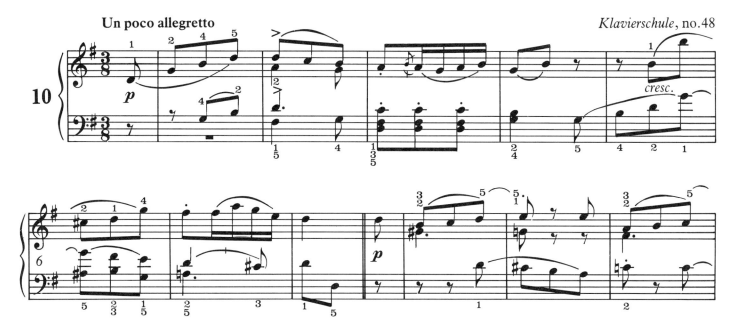

[♪=c.116]

Scherzo in A

Klavierschule, no.45

Rondo in C

Op. 52 no. 6

*In the original edition all acciaccaturas are notated as a semiquaver.

Alla Polacca in B flat

Klavierschule, no.53

Allegretto in C

Klavierschule, no.50

[♩=c.94]

To Alexis

Klavierschule, no.59

Andantino espressivo

*When two notes are connected by a slur, the second must be played short (Hummel's footnote).

Allegro in F

Klavierschule, no.56

AB 1853